It Happened One Pi Day

The Easy Way to Memorize Pi

From Cover:

30 – A <u>Moo</u>se <u>Mi</u>ssing his <u>Mo</u>ss
74 – The <u>Kr</u>aken <u>C</u>rushing a <u>C</u>ar
23 – A <u>No</u>mad <u>N</u>aming a G<u>no</u>me
32 – A <u>Mi</u>ner <u>Mi</u>ning the <u>Moo</u>n
38 – A <u>Mo</u>ver <u>Mo</u>ving a <u>Muf</u>fler
51 – A <u>La</u>dy <u>Le</u>ading a <u>Li</u>ght
42 – An <u>RN</u> <u>Ru</u>nning in the <u>Rai</u>n

Text and Illustrations Copyright © 2017 by Eric Schmidt

Produced by Eric Schmidt
Written by Eric, Michelle, Jasmine, Mae, and Adam Schmidt
Illustrations by Alena Orlova

Printed in the United States of America

First Printing, 2017

It Happened One Pi Day

ISBN 978-0-9994710-1-2

PAO Publishing
www.PAOPublishing.com

You will use this book to Memorize Pi

This book is a guide to memorizing pi. The tricks that you will learn using this book can be used to memorize any series of numbers. You will find that this book makes memorizing pi a very simple task. Each element that you will see in this story is a scene that can be easily remembered (a mnemonic). Each mnemonic is a Major System Person Action Object (PAO) key to a 6-digit number. The sequence of events that occur in the story is called a Memory Palace.

The Trick – The Secret

The secret to mastering a Major System PAO (Person, Action, Object) is to work backwards. The hard way would be to invent or learn a PAO dictionary (usually 00 through 99), and then memorize it, and then use it to memorize numbers. It turns out that the easy way was right there in front of us all along. First, memorize a large number using mnemonics based on a Major System PAO, then you will find that you intuitively know a large portion of the dictionary and can pick it up very quickly.

PAO – Person Action Object

PAO is a method for memorizing numbers. This book uses a two-digit PAO, so there is a Person, an Action, and an Object for each number from 00 to 99.

Example

The sound "N" is substituted for the digit "2", and "M" for "3", so "23" becomes "A Nomad naming a gnome". In any sequence of six digits, any time that you see the digits 23 it will be either the person "Nomad", the action "naming", or it will be the object "gnome", depending on whether it is in the first, second or third place within the six.

General Rules

Remember that any Person, Action, or Object represents two sounds and two digits. For any Person, Action, or Object, when you see a single word, use the first and second consonants that are most prominent to your ear (and underlined within the text). When you find that a Person, Action, or Object is made up of two words, then take the first consonant sound from each of the two words. These rules are not set in stone, but are generally a good guide to the book

Memory Palace

Memory Palace is a technique used to memorize long sequences of numbers. Using this technique, you build a series of familiar places in your mind and then place the things that you want to remember into that context. This book combines a PAO system with a Memory Palace. The book provides a shell and you fill in the details yourself. For example, if the story says "You wake up in your own bed", you should picture your own bed in your own bedroom. Picture the things on your own walls. Imagine the sounds and smells that characterize that space. Make it your own wherever possible.

An older name for the Memory Palace technique is "The method of loci" where *loci* is a Latin word meaning "places". The method is thought to have been already mature and well established by the time of ancient Greece. It was discussed in writings by Cicero. Memory Palace is used to memorize anything from numbers to names to lists of objects. The heart of the technique is to associate the list of things that you want to memorize with another list of things that are already in your spatial memory. In Memory Palace, you build a sequence of familiar places in your mind then place the things that you want to remember into that context.

The Major System

The Major System is a phonetic number system. The system works by associating each of the ten digits to certain consonant sounds. Think of it as a way of assigning a sound to each digit. While not as ancient as Memory Palace, The Major System has been around for a very long time. Early versions of it existed over 400 years ago and the modern form shown here has been in use for nearly 200 years.

In the Major System, each of the ten digits 0 through 9 are assigned one or more consonant sounds. Once you memorize which sounds are associated with which numbers, you can substitute these sounds for the numbers that you are trying to memorize. When you look at the words, it will be the sounds of the letters that lead you to the numbers. There are only 10 of these to remember, but you don't even need to memorize these before you start. You can just jump right into the story and learn the mnemonics one page at a time. After you start to get the hang of it you can refer back to the Major System Key on this page to make it all come together.

When you see this digit	You will use this sound	Why this sound?
0	S or Z	Because zero starts with Z, and S is a lot like Z.
1	T or D	These consonants are very phonetically similar. Each of these, T and D, contain a single "down stroke" when written.
2	N	The shape of the digit 2 is very similar to a lower-case "n".
3	M	The shape of 3 is a lot like an M.
4	R	"Four" and "R" as syllables, both end with sound of "R".
5	L	In Roman Numerals, L is 50. Also, there is a little "L" in the digit 5. 5
6	Sh or Ch or J	6 is used for three different "soft consonant" sounds. Think of Shark, Judge, and Chute.
7	K (or C where it sounds like a K) and sometimes G	The written strokes of a 7 can be a part of a "K"
8	V or F	A lower-case "f" can be written with curves that are similar to an 8, especially in cursive. A digit 8 can be seen to contain a small "V". 8
9	P or B	Flipped, and mirrored, a 9 can easily be a "P" or a "b".

Now it's time to start........

I woke up early that morning. With my eyes still closed and my head still on my pillow, I could feel the warmth of the sun on my face as the day peeked through my window. I sat up with a stretch. My feet touched the floor at the same moment that I opened my eyes. With some alarm I was jarred by one of the strangest sights that anyone has ever laid eyes on. Amazingly and inexplicably, right in front of me sat...

<u>M</u>r. <u>T</u>oad <u>r</u>i<u>d</u>ing a <u>l</u>i<u>p</u>

It was an enormous lip, and clearly one made for riding. Before I was able to react in any way he was off. In a flash he rode that lip right out the door of my room.

3.14159

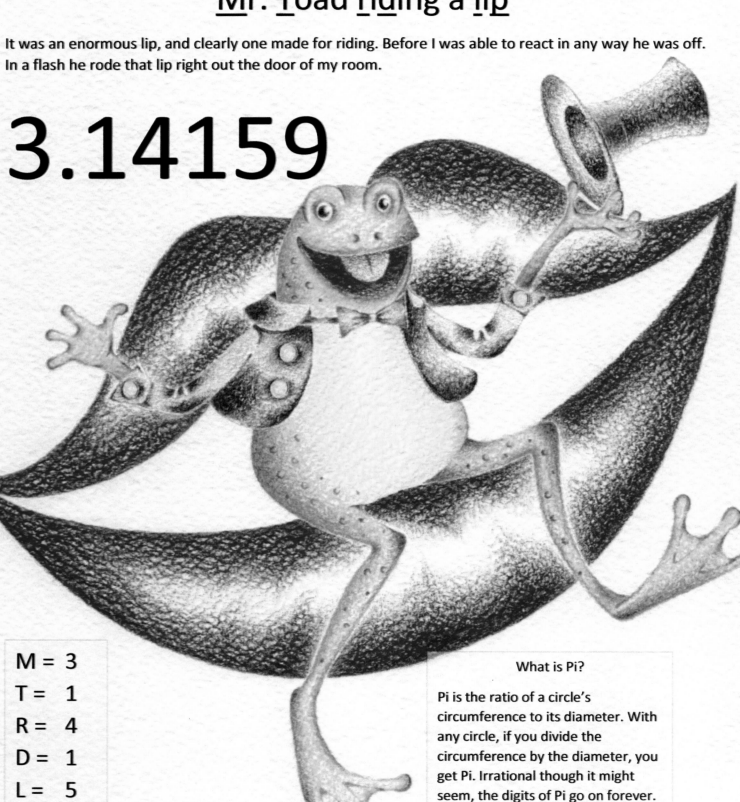

M = 3
T = 1
R = 4
D = 1
L = 5
P = 9

What is Pi?

Pi is the ratio of a circle's circumference to its diameter. With any circle, if you divide the circumference by the diameter, you get Pi. Irrational though it might seem, the digits of Pi go on forever.

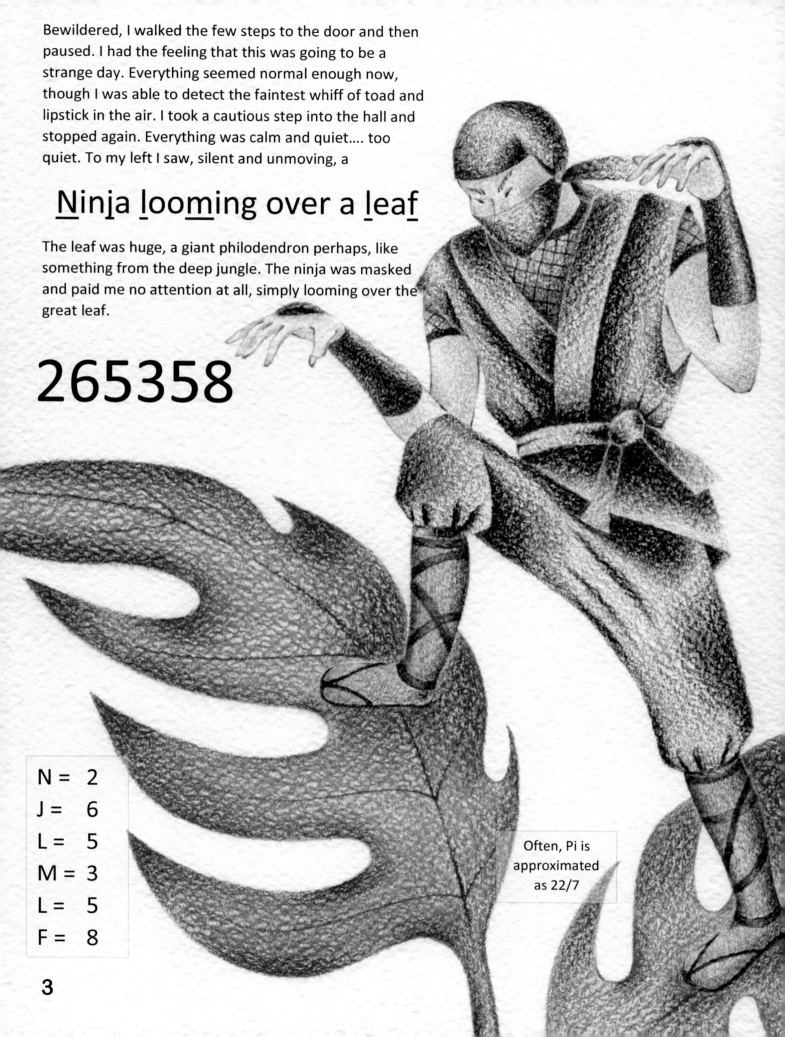

Bewildered, I walked the few steps to the door and then paused. I had the feeling that this was going to be a strange day. Everything seemed normal enough now, though I was able to detect the faintest whiff of toad and lipstick in the air. I took a cautious step into the hall and stopped again. Everything was calm and quiet…. too quiet. To my left I saw, silent and unmoving, a

Ninja looming over a leaf

The leaf was huge, a giant philodendron perhaps, like something from the deep jungle. The ninja was masked and paid me no attention at all, simply looming over the great leaf.

265358

N = 2
J = 6
L = 5
M = 3
L = 5
F = 8

Often, Pi is approximated as 22/7

3

BOOM!

For the space of a few heartbeats I stood as still as the Ninja. I had just decided that I was safe from both Ninja and leaf when the silence was broken by a booming shout. In fact, it was the word "BOOM!" that was shouted. I was startled and shocked. I turned to face the end of the hall and saw that this great BOOM emanated from a cowboy and was not directed at me at all. What I saw was

<u>B</u>illy the <u>K</u>id, <u>B</u>oo<u>m</u>ing a G<u>n</u>o<u>m</u>e

Startled as I had been, I could see that the gnome was his true target. Clearly it had been some sort of a prank. The gnome was far more surprised than I was.

979323

B = 9
K = 7
B = 9
M = 3
N = 2
M = 3

Pi is irrational and transcendental. It is irrational because it cannot be written as a rational, simple fraction (as we saw earlier, 22/7 is close but not exact). Pi is transcendental because it is not algebraic. It is not a root of a nonzero polynomial equation with integer coefficients. Another well-known transcendental number is e – Euler's Number.

I wanted to pretend that this was a normal day. I backed away and then stepped into the kitchen thinking to have coffee or tea. It had just occurred to me that sugar in my drink might be nice on a day like this one, when I saw

The <u>V</u>elveteen <u>R</u>abbit, <u>Sh</u>ining the <u>Sugar</u>

I had read the story about The Velveteen Rabbit, and clearly this was him, come to life and helping in the kitchen.

846264

V = 8
R = 4
Sh = 6
N = 2
Sh = 6
R = 4

Pi is sometimes referred to as
Archimedes' Constant

Archimedes worked for years to approximate the value of pi. He was the first scholar to build a calculation for pi rather than simply estimating it. Archimedes overlaid a circle with polygons and then used one of Euclid's theorems to measure the polygons through an iterative algorithm. He was far ahead of his time. Archimedes calculated that the value of pi is between 3 10/71 and 3 1/7.

I stepped outside with my warm mug thinking that some morning light and some fresh air would help clear my head. Just outside the door, the air was not clear at all. I had to wave away the smell of fumes. I looked down and saw

<u>M</u>iss <u>M</u>oppet, <u>fum</u>igating her <u>neck</u>

She must have gotten herself into some trouble with fleas. I could see them jumping away from the ruff at her neck which she deftly fumigated.

338327

Do you have it to this point?
30 Digits of Pi!

M = 3
M = 3
F = 8
M = 3
N = 2
K = 7

104348/33215
is the most accurate
fraction of Pi

Stepping away from the smell of the flea spray, I took only one step before I stopped, hearing the crunch of a musical instrument and the bark of a three-headed dog. Now, I had never thought to meet any god out of ancient mythology, but when I saw the trident and the crown and the obvious appetite for small wind instruments, I knew that this was

<u>P</u>luto, <u>sn</u>acking on a <u>Fi</u>fe

Now I do not think that every dog needs three heads, but Cerberus sure is cute.

950288

P = 9
L = 5
S = 0
N = 2
F = 8
F = 8

7

Interestingly,
$\sqrt{2} + \sqrt{3} = 3.146$

Taking a few steps toward the front walk, there was a Dojo where no Dojo had been before! And there was an adorable

<u>R</u>at, <u>B</u>aking at the <u>D</u>ojo

419716

3.14 backwards looks like PIE

R = 4
T = 1
B = 9
K = 7
D = 1
J = 6

8

I was almost to the edge of my yard, I sat my mug down near some plants in my garden. I sat down in order to contemplate this very strange day. Suddenly, darting out from behind the greenery, there was

<u>B</u>illy <u>M</u>ink <u>B</u>op<u>p</u>ing <u>m</u>y <u>M</u>ug

939937

He just gave it one good BOP with his walking stick and then he was off.

B = 9
M = 3
B = 9
P = 9
M = 3
G = 7

9

"I prefer pi" is a palindrome

From where I was seated I realized that I could see quite far, much farther that I would have thought. I saw a body of water in the distance. I saw a fine lady in beautiful hat and dress. She was sailing around on a…. On what? It was

A <u>La</u>d<u>y</u>, <u>s</u>ai<u>l</u>ing a <u>fan</u>

510582

She was sailing quite beautifully. The fan provided quite a bit of power. I wondered where she plugged it in.

L =   5
D =   1
S =   0
L =   5
F =   8
N =   2

The square root of 9.869604401 is approximately Pi

I watched her as she sailed. She was having quite an adventure. I saw the Lady sail past a

Spider, crushing a Pear
097494

Wow!
60 Digits of Pi!

Nearby the spider there was a boy named

Riley, Pinning Moss
459230

He was quite busy.

Finally she got to the party.
There was

Grandfather Frog
DJ'ing at a Razor Party
781640

Everyone was having a great time, but with
the noise and the danger of the razors, some
thought that the Sheriff should be called.

However, he was not going to respond, because

The Sheriff of Nottingham
was Fishing for a Nose
628620

And he caught one too!

The danger was real however. A young man from the
Pi Pi Pi fraternity cut himself shaving with
one of the razors so that I could see the

Frat Boy Poofing
his Chin
899862

Poofing it with cotton helped to stem the bleeding.

12

The fine Lady had hopped off of the fan and she was nowhere to be seen. I saw the very helpful

Dr. Frankenstein Mooring the Fan
803482

He used a bowline.

Right next to him, just zipping off her fish tail, was...

Little Mermaid, Running after a Tot
534211

That tot sure was fast.

King Solomon found where the cotton grows. He picked a puff of cotton.

King Solomon is Shaking a Puff
706798

Now it starts to get serious.
102 Digits of Pi!

Someone was needed to fix this safe. It will take a great inventor to bring it back to good working order.

Nikola Tesla, Reviving a Safe
214808

14

Julie had just heard that there is a fair coming to town and she thought that she might like to join. She is teaching herself to juggle so that she can try out for the crew. So we see

Julie Taming a knife   651328

Be careful Julie.

We have another taker. If there is a fair coming then our friend the Nomad would also like to join. He can dance quite well, and he brought the sugar to sweeten the deal.

Nomad, sashaying with Sugar 230664

15

When will we hear that the fair is actually here?

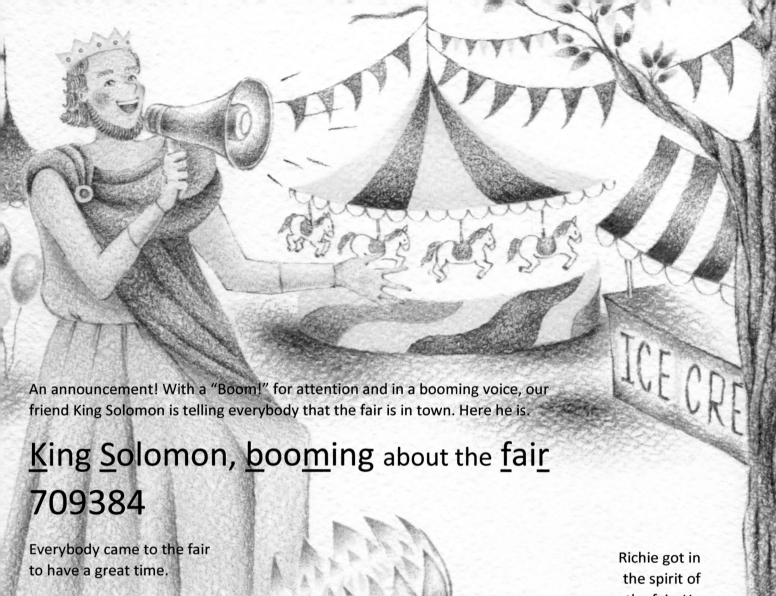

An announcement! With a "Boom!" for attention and in a booming voice, our friend King Solomon is telling everybody that the fair is in town. Here he is.

<u>K</u>ing <u>S</u>olomon, <u>boom</u>ing about the <u>fair</u>
709384

Everybody came to the fair
to have a great time.

Richie got in the spirit of the fair. He can juggle too! Or at least he can spin that lily!

<u>R</u>ichie, <u>sp</u>inning a <u>L</u>ily
460955

Let's follow this water now. I think that this will lead out to open water big enough for a boat.

Moving away from the fair, back out on the water I saw...

A <u>Sai</u>l<u>or</u>, <u>fann</u>ing a G<u>nome</u> 058223

The sailboat is moving right past a big tree on the bank, where

<u>D</u>avy <u>C</u>rockett was <u>n</u>ai<u>l</u>ing a <u>Meal</u> 172535

He wanted to keep his food safe from bears.

The nail did not hold. The bag of food would not be safe from bears, nor from rabbits. The bag fell to the ground and soon enough, there was…

<u>P</u>eter <u>R</u>abbit, <u>sn</u>i<u>ff</u>ing a <u>D</u>o<u>n</u>ut
940812

Speaking of rabbits, here is another. Playing at boxing, here is The

<u>V</u>elveteen <u>R</u>abbit, <u>F</u>igh<u>t</u>ing a <u>T</u>o<u>t</u>
848111

Oh no! I lost
my knife!

Turning my eye again
to the water, I see

The
Kraken,
Losing his
Knife
745028

A little farther along the bank, that adorable little rat has
caught up with me again, I see...

A Rat, snacking on a Kazoo
410270

I see a beautiful fairy helping to cast off a line so that a little dog can sail away. It is...

Tinker Bell, moving a Line
193852

I will cast you off!

I know that dog! I see

Toto, sailing a Lily
110555

Where are you taking that Lily Toto?

Oh no.... We have another chin injury. A razor party was a bad idea. He cut himself and now

Prince Charming is Roaring about his Chin 964462

He's a bit of a whiner.

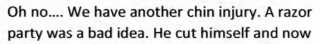

Wake up you plum!

Nobody invited him to the party, but here he is with Prince Charming and trying to wake up all of the fruit in the garden. It is

Napoleon, Reviving a Plum 294895

I sure do miss my muffler!

Overhead, everyone can hear the loudest airplane ever. That airplane must have no muffler at all.
It seems that The

Red Baron is

Missing his Muffler 493038

I'm starting to see that I might be the irrational one. This is a transcendental day.

It's all coming in a rush now, like this

Martian **rushing** through a

Donut   344612

Here sugar......
Here sugar!

and the **Velveteen**

Rabbit, Calling

"**Sugar**"

847564

He was performing a short time ago. Now he seems to be taking a break. Have you ever seen

A **Faun, miming** with **Coffee**

823378

Miss Moppet might have visited the DoJo, because now

Jack is **fumigating**

the **Dojo** 678316

The Sheriff did not catch all of the noses, because here we can see

Abraham **L**inco**l**n, **c**oun**t**ing **n**o**s**es

"One, two, three....
Four score and seven noses."

527120

Here she is again.

Tinker**b**ell, **sp**inning in the **tr**ees 190914

I will revive you, you broken latch!

And...

Long **J**ohn Silver **Re**viving a **L**a**tch** 564856

I will name you Rachel.

She's all that, and she knows it. She definitely thinks that she is the The Queen of **Sheba**

Na**m**ing a **R**oa**ch** 692346

24

Look! I brought back the chute!

So helpful. Everyone is thankful for the

<u>S</u>and <u>M</u>an, <u>Re</u>viving a <u>Chut</u>e 034861

It doesn't look like she is leering to me. She looks pensive if anything.

<u>C</u>inde<u>r</u>ella, <u>l</u>ee<u>r</u>ing at the <u>Moon</u> 045432

I did it. Now I can read it! I have revived this note.

The Jolly Giant is an expert at restoration of document artifacts.

<u>J</u>olly <u>G</u>iant, <u>Re</u>viving a <u>Not</u>e 664821

Boom...

No fleas now. What in the world does she hope to accomplish by booming the cheese?

<u>M</u>iss <u>M</u>oppet, <u>boom</u>ing, <u>Chee<u>s</u>e 339360

I will not sing. I choose narration!

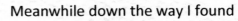

Meanwhile down the way I found **C**aptain **N**emo, **C**hoo**s**ing **N**a**rr**ation 726024

Elite Status!
300 Digits of Pi!

And in a state of sublime calm, here was The **B**u**dd**ha, **r**i**d**ing a **N**e**ck** 914127

And even though she spoke only the language of the geese, I listened to **M**other **G**oose, **N**a**rr**ating with a **L**ea**f** 372458

This wacky king just keeps showing up. Now he is dancing with a dairy product. It's **K**ing **S**olomon, **sa**s**h**aying with **C**hee**s**e 700660

What does a muskrat love? Well I know what this one loves to do.

<u>J</u>erry <u>M</u>uskrat is <u>till</u>ing for a <u>L</u>eaf
631558

I might not be that good at the fiddle, but I crush on the fife!

This fiddler should give up his dislike for other instruments. We should not have to see a <u>F</u>iddler, <u>cr</u>ushing a <u>Fif</u>e 817488

She sure loves that pan! I hope her nose is clean because

<u>T</u>iger <u>L</u>ily is <u>nuzz</u>ling a <u>P</u>an 152092

Good job spider! It looks great! I've never seen a

<u>Sp</u>ider, <u>Shin</u>ing a <u>F</u>an 096282

Look at the look that pony is giving that spool. Why is a

Pony, leering at a Spool 925409

He already lost his bag of donuts, now

Davy Crockett is tilling some Matches 171536

Juliet, my Juliet, come play football with me.

Romeo, Shaking a Football 436789

These matches did not work on the moon.

Neil Armstrong, Posing with Matches 259036

28

Usually found at sea, here he is on a teeter-totter. We see

<u>S</u>inbad the <u>S</u>ailor, <u>tee</u>tering with

a <u>M</u>e<u>me</u>   001133

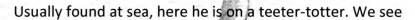

Our other sailor used to play a musical instrument. He sure misses it now. The

<u>Sai</u>lor is

<u>mi</u>ss<u>i</u>ng his

<u>L</u>y<u>r</u>e

053054

Everybody loves roaches. This is

<u>V</u>incent <u>V</u>an Gogh, <u>nu</u>zz<u>l</u>ing a <u>R</u>oa<u>ch</u>

882046

She has deft hands and far more interest in personal comfort

than in automotive mechanics. This is <u>Ju</u>l<u>i</u>e,

k<u>n</u>i<u>tt</u>ing a <u>M</u>uffler

652138

I find myself intrigued. These new friends seem to be recurring. King Solomon and the cute little rat come back again and again in this dream. Am I going in a circle? Now I see

a <u>Rat</u>, <u>rush</u>ing with a <u>Pl</u>um 414695

And here is <u>Tinker Bell</u>, <u>ri</u>ding on a <u>Light</u> 194151

A new Doctor! It's Dr. <u>J</u>ekyll, <u>sp</u>inning in a <u>Room</u> 160943

Very few have done this. 402 Digits of Pi!

The Buddha is now gone. I see

a <u>Moos</u>e, <u>lick</u>ing a <u>N</u>eck 305727

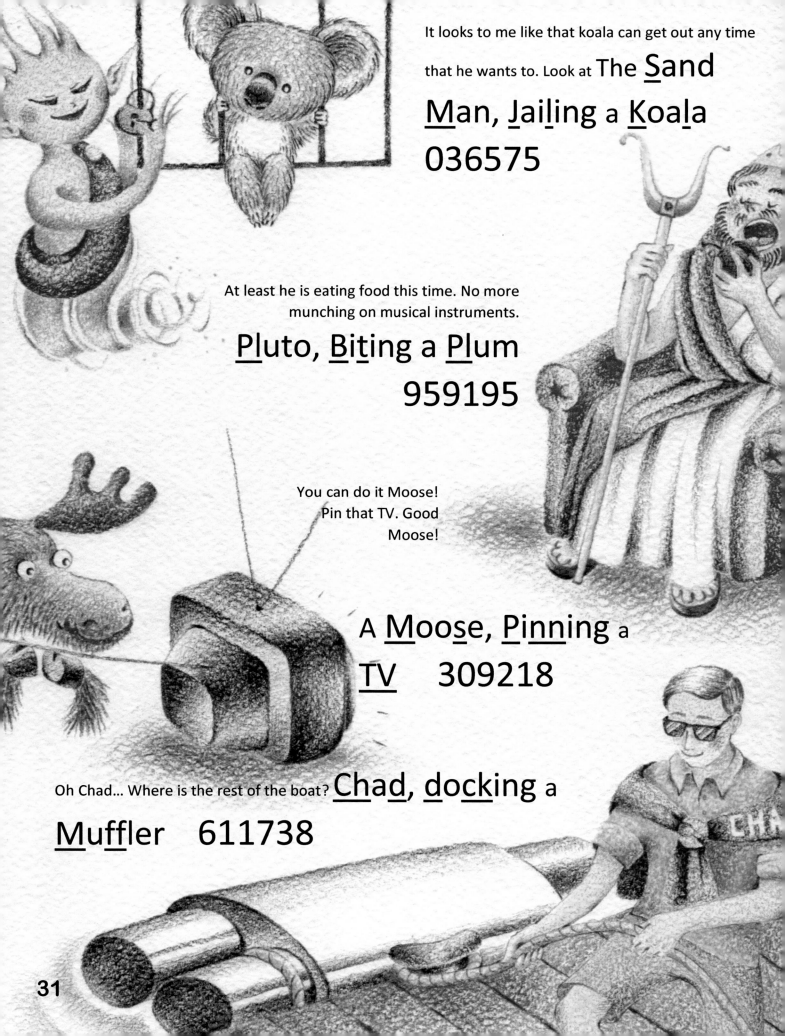

It looks to me like that koala can get out any time that he wants to. Look at The Sand Man, Jailing a Koala
036575

At least he is eating food this time. No more munching on musical instruments.
Pluto, Biting a Plum
959195

You can do it Moose! Pin that TV. Good Moose!

A Moose, Pinning a TV 309218

Oh Chad... Where is the rest of the boat? Chad, docking a Muffler 611738

31

What are you digging for Tink? I see that you have already found gems. What do you hope to find?

Tinker Bell is Mining for a Chute 193261

BOOM!

Be careful Davy! Don't drop that rock. You have a long hike ahead of you. Try not to Boom your Toes!

Davy Crockett, booming his Toes 179310

Ah. Hello Fine Lady. That's a beautiful lyre that you are tree farming with. I think that I know the sailor that would like to get it back.

A Lady, Tree Farming with a Lyre 511854

This roach is far too fast for Dr. Frankenstein. He will never be able to crush this roach.

Dr. Frankenstein, crushing a Roach 807446

TREE FARM

Oh no. You will not!!

32

What does this nomad do when he is not naming gnomes?

Nomad, Keeping a Peach   237996

Oh, you're a peach, you are.

Why do you want that latch so bad President Nixon?

Nixon, Robbing a Latch 274956

Ha! I got the latch!

Hi Grandma. You don't look much like my Grandma but I know who you are! Is this a parade or are you just trying to save that fife from deities and fiddlers?

Grandma, Leading a Fife 735188

C'mon Fife!

Here is the mighty Lion King. He is having a slow day. He might even be asleep.

The Lion King, leaning on a Cane 575272

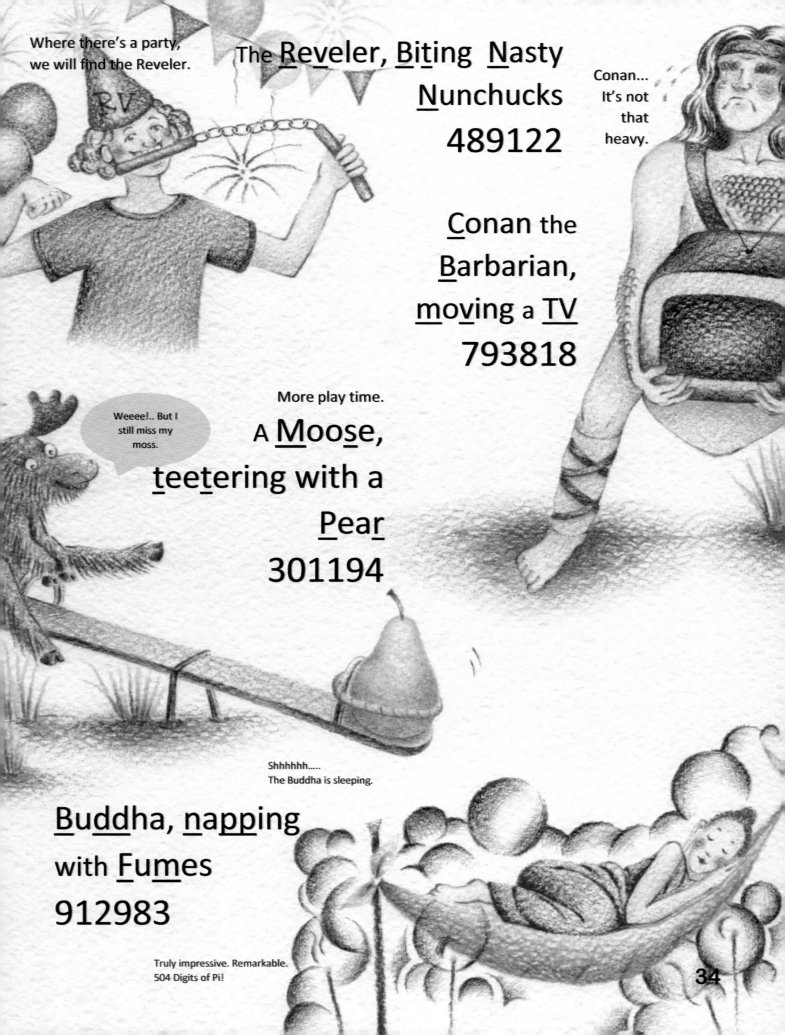

Where there's a party, we will find the Reveler.

The <u>R</u>eveler, <u>B</u>i<u>t</u>ing <u>N</u>asty Nunchucks
489122

Conan... It's not that heavy.

<u>C</u>onan the <u>B</u>arbarian, <u>m</u>o<u>v</u>ing a <u>TV</u>
793818

Weeee!.. But I still miss my moss.

More play time.
A <u>Moos</u>e, <u>t</u>ee<u>t</u>ering with a <u>P</u>ea<u>r</u>
301194

Shhhhhh.....
The Buddha is sleeping.

<u>B</u>ud<u>d</u>ha, <u>n</u>a<u>pp</u>ing with <u>F</u>u<u>m</u>es
912983

Truly impressive. Remarkable. 504 Digits of Pi!

34

Now we have some action! There's a new Marshall in town. From now on, we gamble with matches that have been to the moon.

The <u>Ma</u>r<u>sh</u>all, <u>G</u>a<u>m</u>bling with <u>Match</u>es
367336

<u>Ne</u>ro, <u>R</u>oa<u>s</u>ting a <u>J</u>ewel
244065

<u>J</u>olly <u>G</u>iant, <u>R</u>oa<u>m</u>ing with a <u>S</u>a<u>f</u>e
664308

Jimmy <u>S</u>kunk, k<u>n</u>i<u>tt</u>ing a <u>M</u>o<u>p</u>
602139

I can hear that your muffler is repaired, but why are you waving that mop?

I'm in a big hurry!

Red Baron, rushing with a Mop

494639

Lincoln went move by move and narrated the entire game to us.

Lincoln, narrating a Game

522473

I look spectacular with this kazoo.

Count Dracula, Posing with a Kazoo

719070

Memory training is very important for my health, I must remember where I am keeping this fudge.

Nikola Tesla, Keeping some Fudge

217986

That silly spider has absconded with our only kazoo.

A <u>Sp</u>ider, <u>R</u>oa<u>m</u>ing with a <u>Ka</u><u>z</u>oo
094370

His second great passion was weaving.

<u>Ni</u><u>x</u>on, <u>Ki</u><u>ss</u>ing a <u>L</u>oo<u>m</u>
277053

Great docking job pony!

A <u>P</u>ony, <u>d</u>o<u>ck</u>ing at a <u>D</u>ance <u>C</u>lub
921717

No more fishing for me. I am going to dance the night away!

BOOM!

<u>Sh</u>eriff of <u>N</u>ottingham, <u>b</u>oo<u>m</u>ing at a <u>D</u>ance <u>C</u>lub   629317

Thank you so much for reading this book. We hope that you have had a great time. We hope that you can now recite or write down many digits of Pi. Maybe 600 of them.

Now, please come visit us online!

Scan the following:

To visit: http://www.ItHappenedOnePiDay.com

For fun things to do. Learn more of Pi. Plug in your own numbers and use PAO to learn them!

Our Person Action Object Vocabulary

Number	Person		Action	Object
00	Sinbad the Sailor		slicing	Scissors
01	Seven Dwarfs		siding	Sod
02	The Sun		snacking	Snails
03	Sand Man		smacking	a semi
04	Cinderella		searing	Sriracha
05	Sailor		sailing	Sail
06	Sushi Chef		sashaying	Sash
07	Santa Claus		scooting	Skis
08	Sigmund Freud		sniffing	Safe
09	Spider		spinning	Spool
10	Tom Sawyer		toasting	Toes
11	Toto		teetering	Tot
12	Diner		dining	Donut
13	Three Musketeers		taming	Team
14	Theodore Roosevelt		touring	Tree
15	Tiger Lily		tilling	Tools
16	Dr. Jekyll		DJ'ing	Dojo
17	Davy Crockett		docking	dance club
18	Tooth Fairy		tree farming	TV
19	Tinker Bell		tubing	Table
20	Einstein		nuzzling	Nose
21	Nikola Tesla		knitting	Note
22	Nanny		nay naying	nasty nunchucks
23	Nomad		naming	gnome
24	Nero		narrating	narration
25	Neil Armstrong		nailing	Nail
26	Ninja		nudging	notch
27	Nixon		knocking	neck
28	Knave		knifing	knife
29	Napoleon		napping	nap
30	Moose		missing	moss
31	Mr. Toad		mounting	mat
32	Miner		Mining	moon
33	Miss Moppet		miming	meme
34	Martian		mooring	mare
35	Mulan		mailing	meal
36	Marshall		munching	matches
37	Mother Goose		making	mug
38	mover		moving	muffler
39	Mabel		moping	mop
40	Russ		roasting	razor
41	Rat		riding	root
42	Registered Nurse		running	rain
43	Romeo		roaming	room
44	Red Riding Hood		roaring	rear
45	Riley		reeling	rail
46	Richie		rushing	roach
47	Robinson Crusoe		rocking	rock
48	Reveler		reviving	R.V.
49	Red Baron		robbing	ribs

#	Name		Action	Object
50	Lazy Susan		losing	Laser
51	Lady		leading	light
52	Lincoln		leaning	Line
53	Little Mermaid		looming	Loom
54	Larry		leering	Lyre
55	Lola		LOL'ing (Laughing Out Loud)	Lily
56	Long John Silver		lashing	Latch
57	Lion King		licking	Lake
58	Levi		loving	Leaf
59	Love Bird		looping	Lip
60	Jimmy Skunk		choosing	cheese
61	Chad		chatting	Chute
62	Sheriff of Nottingham		shining	Chin
63	Jerry Muskrat		jamming	Jam
64	Shark		sharing	Sugar
65	Julie		jailing	Jewel
66	Jolly Giant		shushing	Judge
67	Jack		shaking	Shack
68	Jack Frost		shoving	shovel
69	Sheba		shaping	sheep
70	King Solomon		kissing	Kazoo
71	Count Dracula		counting	Kite
72	Captain Nemo		canning	Cane
73	Grandma		gambling	Game
74	Kraken		crushing	Car
75	Kelly		calling	koala
76	Coach		coaching	couch
77	Captain Kidd		kicking	cake
78	Grandfather Frog		coughing	coffee
79	Conan the Barbarian		keeping	cab
80	Frankenstein (Dr.)		fussing	face
81	Fiddler		fighting	foot
82	Faun		fanning	fan
83	Family Man		fumigating	fumes
84	Velveteen Rabbit		firing	fair
85	Flea		falling	foal
86	Fish		fishing	fudge
87	Viking		vacuuming	vacuum
88	Vincent Van Gogh		freeforming	fife
89	Frat Boy		flipping	football
90	Perseus		posing	posse
91	Buddha		biting	beet
92	Pony		pinning	pan
93	Billy Mink		booming	beam
94	Peter Rabbit		praying	pear
95	Pluto		plowing	plum
96	Prince Charming		punching	peach
97	Billy the Kid		baking	bike
98	Brer Fox		poofing	puff
99	Black Beauty		bopping	baby

Study Guide – Complete PAO Mnemonic List for Pi

3.14159	Mr. Toad, riding, Lip
265358	Ninja, looming, Leaf
979323	Billy the Kid, booming, Gnome
846264	Velveteen Rabbit, Shining, Sugar
338327	Miss Moppet, fumigating, Neck
950288	Pluto, snacking, Fife
419716	Rat, Baking, Dojo
939937	Billy Mink, Bopping, Mug
510582	Lady, sailing, Fan
097494	Spider, crushing, Pear
459230	Riley, Pinning, Moss
781640	Grandfather Frog, DJ'ing, Razor
628620	Sheriff of Nottingham, Fishing, Nose
899862	Frat Boy, Poofing, Chin
803482	Frankenstein, mooring, Fan
534211	Little Mermaid, Running, Tot
706798	King Solomon, Shaking, Puff
214808	Nikola Tesla, Reviving, Safe
651328	Julie, taming, Knife
230664	Nomad, sashaying, Sugar
709384	King Solomon, booming, Fair
460955	Richie, spinning, Lilly
058223	Sailor, fanning, Gnome
172535	Davy Crockett, nailing, Meal
940812	Peter Rabbit, sniffing, Donut
848111	Velveteen Rabbit, Fighting, Tot
745028	Kraken, Losing, Knife
410270	Rat, snacking, Kazoo
193852	Tinker Bell, moving, Line
110555	Toto, sailing, Lilly
964462	Prince Charming, Roaring, Chin
294895	Napoleon, Reviving, Plum
493038	Red Baron, missing, Muffler
196442	Tinker Bell, sharing, Rain
881097	Vincent VanGogh, toasting, Bike
566593	Long John Silver, Jailing, Beam
344612	Martian, rushing, Donut
847564	Velveteen Rabbit, Calling, Sugar
823378	Faun, miming, Coffee
678316	Jack, fumigating, Dojo
527120	Lincoln, counting, Nose
190914	Tinker Bell, spinning, Tree
564856	Long John Silver, Reviving, Latch
692346	Sheba, naming, Roach
034861	Sand Man, Reviving, Chute
045432	Cinderella, leering, Moon
664821	Jolly Giant, Reviving, Note
339360	Miss Moppet, booming, Cheese
726024	Captain Nemo, Choosing, Narration
914127	Buddha, riding, Neck
372458	Mother Goose, narrating, Leaf

700660	King Solomon, sashaying, Cheese
631558	Jerry Muskrat, tilling, Leaf
817488	Fiddler, crushing, Fife
152092	Tiger Lily, nuzzling, Pan
096282	Spider, Shining, Fan
925409	Pony, leering, Spool
171536	Davy Crockett, tilling, Matches
436789	Romeo, Shaking, Football
259036	Neil Armstrong, Posing, Matches
001133	Sinbad the Sailor, teetering, Meme
053054	Sailor, missing, Lyre
882046	Vincent VanGogh, nuzzling, Roach
652138	Julie, knitting, Muffler
414695	Rat, rushing, Plum
194151	Tinker Bell, riding, Light
160943	Dr. Jekyll, spinning, Room
305727	Moose, licking, Neck
036575	Sand Man, Jailing, Koala
959195	Pluto, Biting, Plum
309218	Moose, Pinning, TV
611738	Chad, docking, Muffler
193261	Tinker Bell, Mining, Chute
179310	Davy Crockett, booming, Toes
511854	Lady, Tree Farming, Lyre
807446	Frankenstein, crushing, Roach
237996	Nomad , Keeping, Peach
274956	Nixon, Robbing, Latch
735188	Grandma, leading, Fife
575272	Lion King, leaning, Cane
489122	Reveler, Biting, Nasty Nunchucks
793818	Conan the Barbarian, moving, TV
301194	Moose, teetering, Pear
912983	Buddha, napping, Fumes
367336	Marshall, Gambling, Matches
244065	Nero, Roasting, Jewel
664308	Jolly Giant, Roaming, Safe
602139	Jimmy Skunk, knitting, Mop
494639	Red Baron, rushing, Mop
522473	Lincoln, narrating, Game
719070	Count Dracula, Posing, Kazoo
217986	Nikola Tesla, Keeping, Fudge
094370	Spider, Roaming, Kazoo
277053	Nixon, Kissing, Loom
921717	Pony, docking, Dance Club
629317	Sheriff of Nottingham, booming, Dance Club
675238	Jack, leaning, Muffler
467481	Richie, crushing, Foot
846766	Velveteen Rabbit, Shaking, Judge
940513	Peter Rabbit, sailing, Team

Study Guide – Practice Template – Try to write Pi when given the "Person" only

	"Person"	Count of Digits	Write 6 digits here			"Person"		
1 -	Mr. Toad	6			51 -	Mother Goose	306	
2 -	Ninja	12			52 -	King Solomon	312	
3 -	Billy the Kid	18			53 -	Jerry Muskrat	318	
4 -	Velveteen Rabbit	24			54 -	Fiddler	324	
5 -	Miss Moppet	30			55 -	Tiger Lily	330	
6 -	Pluto	36			56 -	Spider	336	
7 -	Rat	42			57 -	Pony	342	
8 -	Billy Mink	48			58 -	Davy Crockett	348	
9 -	Lady	54			59 -	Romeo	354	
10 -	Spider	60			60 -	Neil Armstrong	360	
11 -	Riley	66			61 -	Sinbad the Sailor	366	
12 -	Grandfather Frog	72			62 -	Sailor	372	
13 -	Sheriff of Nottingham	78			63 -	Vincent VanGogh	378	
14 -	Frat Boy	84			64 -	Julie	384	
15 -	Frankenstein	90			65 -	Rat	390	
16 -	Little Mermaid	96			66 -	Tinker Bell	396	
17 -	King Solomon	102			67 -	Dr. Jekyll	402	
18 -	Nikola Tesla	108			68 -	Moose	408	
19 -	Julie	114			69 -	Sand Man	414	
20 -	Nomad	120			70 -	Pluto	420	
21 -	King Solomon	126			71 -	Moose	426	
22 -	Richie	132			72 -	Chad	432	
23 -	Sailor	138			73 -	Tinker Bell	438	
24 -	Davy Crockett	144			74 -	Davy Crockett	444	
25 -	Peter Rabbit	150			75 -	Lady	450	
26 -	Velveteen Rabbit	156			76 -	Frankenstein	456	
27 -	Kraken	162			77 -	Nomad	462	
28 -	Rat	168			78 -	Nixon	468	
29 -	Tinker Bell	174			79 -	Grandma	474	
30 -	Toto	180			80 -	Lion King	480	
31 -	Prince Charming	186			81 -	Reveler	486	
32 -	Napoleon	192			82 -	Conan the Barbarian	492	
33 -	Red Baron	198			83 -	Moose	498	
34 -	Tinker Bell	204			84 -	Buddha	504	
35 -	Vincent VanGogh	210			85 -	Marshall	510	
36 -	Long John Silver	216			86 -	Nero	516	
37 -	Martian	222			87 -	Jolly Giant	522	
38 -	Velveteen Rabbit	228			88 -	Jimmy Skunk	528	
39 -	Faun	234			89 -	Red Baron	534	
40 -	Jack	240			90 -	Lincoln	540	
41 -	Lincoln	246			91 -	Count Dracula	546	
42 -	Tinker Bell	252			92 -	Nikola Tesla	552	
43 -	Long John Silver	258			93 -	Spider	558	
44 -	Sheba	264			94 -	Nixon	564	
45 -	Sand Man	270			95 -	Pony	570	
46 -	Cinderella	276			96 -	Sheriff of Nottingham	576	
47 -	Jolly Giant	282			97 -	Jack	582	
48 -	Miss Moppet	288			98 -	Richie	588	
49 -	Captain Nemo	294			99 -	Velveteen Rabbit	594	
50 -	Buddha	300			100 -	Peter Rabbit	600	

(Copy this page to practice)

Study Guide – Practice

Template – Try to write Pi in three columns

as shown here:

3.14159	881097	305727
265358	566593	036575
979323	344612	959195
846264	847564	309218
338327	823378	611738
950288	678316	193261
419716	527120	179310
939937	190914	511854
510582	564856	807446
097494	692346	237996
459230	034861	274956
781640	045432	735188
628620	664821	575272
899862	339360	489122
803482	726024	793818
534211	914127	301194
706798	372458	912983
214808	700660	367336
651328	631558	244065
230664	817488	664308
709384	152092	602139
460955	096282	494639
058223	925409	522473
172535	171536	719070
940812	436789	217986
848111	259036	094370
745028	001133	277053
410270	053054	921717
193852	882046	629317
110555	652138	675238
964462	414695	467481
294895	194151	846766
493038	160943	940513
196442		

3.14159

__53__

____23

84____

____88

____

____

51__82

____

____

62____

____

____82

____

____

21____

____

____

____

____55

____

____

____

____

74____

____

____

11____

____

____

____38

19____

88____

____

____

____64

____

____

19____

____

____

04____

____

____

____

37____

____

____

____

____82

____

____

__90__

00__33

____

____

____

41____

____

____

____

____

30____

____

____10

____

__79__

____

____

__52__

____

____

36____

____

____

____

____

____

__90__

____

____

____

____38

____

94____

(Copy this page to practice)